THE MUSIC IN

KING ARTHUR

A DRAMATIC OPERA (1691)

The Words by
JOHN DRYDEN

The music by

HENRY PURCELL

EDITED BY MARGARET LAURIE

VOCAL SCORE

NOVELLO & COMPANY LIMITED

Borough Green   Sevenoaks   Kent

PREFACE

Dryden wrote the 'dramatic opera' of *King Arthur* in 1684 as a piece of political propaganda in support of Charles II; it was not, however, set to music until after the Revolution of 1688 had brought William and Mary to the throne, and the text had apparently to be somewhat altered. It was first produced in the summer of 1691, with great success.

'Opera' in seventeenth-century England did not necessarily mean a work set to music throughout, but rather a work in which music, drama and spectacle were combined. Dryden's *King Arthur* was of this kind, and since he held that only supernatural beings (or heroes) and their worshippers on the one hand, or shepherds, servants etc. on the other could properly express themselves in song, most of the action takes place in speech, despite his real effort to integrate the music into the drama. Ideally, this work should be presented in full on the stage, but it is long by modern standards and requires elaborate production. A concert performance of the music alone will often be more practical; in such a performance the music will be better understood if it is placed in its dramatic context; for this purpose a synopsis of the drama for narration is supplied in this edition.

The principal sources used for this edition were: St. Michael's College, Tenbury, MS 785 (containing Act I only); Royal Academy of Music, London, MS XXXIVB; Oriel College, Oxford, MS UA 35; Bibliothèque du Conservatoire, Paris, Rès. F.202; British Museum, add. MSS 30839, 39565-7, *Ayres for the Theatre* (1697) and contemporary single-sheet songs. These and subsidiary sources are described more fully in the Purcell Society Edition of the full score. I should like to thank the authorities concerned for granting access to their material.

Although certain items may have been cut in performance, and Purcell certainly did not follow Dryden's text exactly, it is clear that none of the main manuscripts is complete; Act V is in a particularly muddled state: for instance, 'Your hay it is mowed' has to be supplied from other sources and the setting which we have of 'Saint George' may not be by Purcell at all. There is a considerable amount of instrumental music associated with the work whose exact position is unknown; on the other hand there is no known music for the scene in Act III where Philadell cures Emmeline's blindness. In this edition I have placed all the known music in the places where I think it was most likely performed, but the reconstruction is only conjectural as far as the opening instrumental pieces, the act tunes and the instrumental versions of some songs are concerned. This reconstruction is discussed more fully in the Purcell Society Edition of the full score.

Tempo and expression marks in English are original, in Italian editorial; notes and ornaments in small characters are editorial. Suggestions made in footnotes are purely editorial if followed by (Ed.), otherwise they are derived from subsidiary sources. Similarly, *ossia* in square brackets are editorial, without them come from subsidiary sources. The continuo part was written with the harpsichord in mind, although expression marks from the voice parts are written into it for the player's guidance.

The notation of rhythm in the seventeenth century was not exact, many subtleties being deliberately left to the performers. Double-dotting of crotchets was an accepted convention, and its use is sometimes, though by no means always, obligatory. The application of the French *notes inégales* to English music is far less clear. It seems likely that the *lourer* (in which the first of a pair of quavers was lengthened and the second shortened) was used quite often. The *couler* (where ♩ was performed as ♪.) was much less frequent, but there is a certain amount of evidence to suggest that it was sometimes intended when quavers are slurred in pairs in instrumental music, particularly in a descending figure with the first note dissonant. In songs with voices repeating or imitating such instrumental phrases, these rhythms would naturally be carried over into the voice parts. Although these variations in rhythm mainly affect quavers, they can also be applied to crotchets in quick $\frac{3}{2}$ or $\frac{6}{4}$ movements, or to semiquavers in in very slow movements. Some rhythmical alterations have been suggested by the use of rhythm signs above the staves; they are, of course, largely optional, and similar rhythms could be used in other places at the discretion of the performers. Certain such alterations (usually double-dotting) have been incorporated into the keyboard reduction where this facilitated notation. In all cases of rhythmical alteration, the rhythms suggested are only approximations; the precise relationship between the two notes concerned will vary with context; ♩♪ will often be closer to ♪♩ , for example. In triple time, the two bars before a main cadence should sometimes be performed as one $\frac{3}{2}$ bar, not two $\frac{3}{4}$ bars; this is indicated by $\frac{3}{2}$ above the keyboard part.

Janet Beat informs me that the wavy line used in 'What power art thou' and 'See, see we assemble' in Act III was a recognised instrumental sign indicating a pulsation of volume on a single note. Singers may achieve the desired effect by singing each group of three repeated quavers as one continuous note but with a fresh accent on each quaver. (The sign is discussed further in the Foreword of the full score). The same effect is required in the accompanying string parts throughout both movements and in the dance following the chorus, but this has not been indicated here since it is impossible to play on the keyboard. The speed of the chorus should be fast enough to make the 'chatter's (with strongly pronounced 't's) sound like chattering teeth; the Cold Genius's solo may be a bit slower, but probably not very much.

The work as staged requires a large number of soloists, though even in the original performance there was a considerable amount of doubling up. In concert performances the work can be performed with a minimum of Soprano I, Soprano II, Countertenor, Tenor and Bass soloists, though a third soprano is desirable. If no countertenor is available, then the countertenor solos can be sung by another tenor, but in this case an alto will be needed as well for some of the ensembles. The orchestra consists of recorders, oboes (preferably with cor anglais and bassoon) trumpets, strings and continuo.

MARGARET LAURIE

NARRATION

(The words in inverted commas are those intended to be spoken by the Narrator)
Nos. 1-4

ACT I

'The Britons under King Arthur have, with the aid of the magician Merlin, driven the Saxons back as far as Kent. Now, on St. George's Day, they prepare for the final battle. King Arthur takes leave of his betrothed, the blind Emmeline. Meanwhile the Saxon king, Oswald, with the assistance of his magician Osmond and the evil spirit Grimbald, prepare for the battle by making animal and human sacrifices to propitiate their gods, Woden, Thor and Freya:'

Nos. 5-9

'The battle is won by the Britons, who celebrate their victory with a song of triumph:'

Nos. 10-11

ACT II

'Grimbald, disguised as a shepherd, attempts to lead astray the Britons who are pursuing the fleeing Oswald, but Merlin sends the airy spirit, Philadell, with a company of other spirits, to rescue them:'

No. 12

'Grimbald, realising the power of song, decides to compete:'

No. 13

'They are about to follow Grimbald, but Philadell's spirits sing again:'

No. 14

'Grimbald, defeated, sinks with a flash, and Philadell and the Spirits, with the Britons in their midst, go off singing:'

No. 15

'Meanwhile Emmeline, awaiting King Arthur's return in the British camp, is entertained by shepherds and shepherdesses:'

Nos. 16-18

'Oswald, stumbling by chance upon the camp, seizes Emmeline and bears her away. Arthur demands her return, but Oswald refuses, even when offered half the kingdom, for he too is in love with her.'

No. 19 [*This may be played after no. 18 or before no. 20 if desired*]

ACT III

'The Britons attempt to rescue Emmeline by force, but are driven back by the strength of Osmond's spells. Philadell and Arthur manage to penetrate the enchanted wood surrounding Oswald's castle and reach Emmeline. Philadell cures her blindness, but they are unable to free her and retreat when Osmond approaches. Osmond, having imprisoned Oswald, tries to win Emmeline for himself, but she, revolted by his appearance, freezes in horror; he tries (vainly) to win her favour by showing her a masque depicting the power of love to thaw frozen people. The scene opens on a prospect of winter in frozen countries:'

Nos. 20-30

ACT IV

'Merlin brings Arthur to the enchanted wood, warning him of its perils. First, two sirens rise out of a stream:'

No. 31

'Arthur resists the lazy pleasure trickling through his veins and presses on. Nymphs and Sylvans make a fresh attempt to seduce him:'

No. 32

'Again he resists and strikes the largest tree in the wood with his sword. Grimbald appears from it in the shape of Emmeline, but just as Arthur is about to embrace his supposed betrothed, Philadell appears and stops him. Arthur then breaks the spell by felling the tree, and Philadell drags Grimbald away.'

No. 33 [*This may be played after no. 32 if desired*]

ACT V

'The Britons at last manage to capture Oswald's castle. As a last resort, Osmond frees Oswald to fight a duel with King Arthur. This Arthur wins.'

No. 34

'Arthur is now reunited with his Emmeline; Osmond is carried away to the dungeons. Oswald, however, is bidden to join the Britons and watch a masque, put on by Merlin, to celebrate 'the wealth, the loves, the glories of our isle' in future ages, when Saxon and Briton shall become one people. First we see the British ocean in a storm. Aeolus in a cloud above sings:'

No. 35

'The scene opens and discovers a calm sea; an island arises with Britannia seated upon it with fishermen at her feet. First are sung the praises of Britain's natural resources: her fish, her sheep, her crops:'

Nos. 36-39

'Then Venus enters, followed by a pair of young lovers:'

Nos. 40-41

'Finally the scene opens above and discovers the order of the Garter. Honour and the Chorus sing:'
Nos. 42-43

CONTENTS

			Page
1	First Music	Chaconne	1
2	Second Music	Overture	5
3		Air	8
4	Overture		8
5	ACT I	Recitative (Tenor & Bass) & Chorus, 'Woden first to thee'	11
6		Recitative (Tenor), 'The white horse neigh'd' & Duet (Countertenor & Tenor), 'To Woden thanks we render'	14
7		Recitative (Soprano), 'The lot is cast'	18
8		Chorus, 'Brave souls'	19
9		Song (Countertenor) & Chorus, 'I call'	25
10		Song (Tenor) & Chorus, 'Come if you dare'	31
11	First Act Tune	Song-tune, 'Come if you dare'	42
12	ACT II, Scene 1	Song (Soprano) & Double Chorus, 'Hither this way'	43
13		Song (Bass), 'Let not a moonborn elf'	51
14		Double Chorus, 'Hither this way'	54
15		Septet & Chorus, 'Come, follow me'	57
16	ACT II, Scene 2	Song (Tenor) & Chorus, 'How blest are shepherds'	68
17		Duet (2 Sopranos), 'Shepherd, shepherd, leave decoying'	73
18		Chorus, 'Come shepherds' & Hornpipe	76
19	Second Act Tune	Air	80
20	ACT III	Prelude	82
21		Recitative (Soprano), 'What ho!'	82
22		Song (Bass), 'What power art thou'	83
23		Song (Soprano), 'Thou doting fool'	85
24		Song (Bass), 'Great love'	87
25		Recitative (Soprano), 'No part of my dominion'	89
26		Prelude	89
27		Chorus, 'See, see, we assemble' & Dance	91
28		Song (Soprano) & Chorus, ' 'Tis I that have warm'd ye'	95
29		Duet (Soprano & Bass), 'Sound a parley'	103
30	Third Act Tune	Hornpipe	110
31	ACT IV	Duet (2 Sopranos), 'Two daughters'	111
32		Passacaglia: Song (Countertenor) & Chorus, 'How happy the lover'; Duet (Soprano & Bass), Trios & Chorus, 'For love ev'ry creature'	115

33	Fourth Act Tune	Air	130
34	ACT V	Consort of Trumpets: Trumpet Tune	131
35		Song (Bass), 'Ye blust'ring brethren'	131
36		Symphony	135
37		Duet (Soprano & Bass) & Chorus, 'Round thy coast'	136
38		Trio (Countertenor, Tenor & Bass), 'For folded flocks'	140
39		Song (Tenor) & Trio (Tenor & 2 Basses), 'Your hay it is mow'd' & Dance	144
40		Song (Soprano), 'Fairest isle'	147
41		Dialogue (Soprano & Bass), 'You say 'tis love'	150
42		Warlike consort: Trumpet tune	158
43		Song (Soprano) & Chorus, 'Saint George'	159

KING ARTHUR

FIRST MUSIC

CHACONNE

Henry Purcell

MADE IN ENGLAND

SECOND MUSIC

OVERTURE

* C may be ♯ (Ed.).

8

AIR

OVERTURE

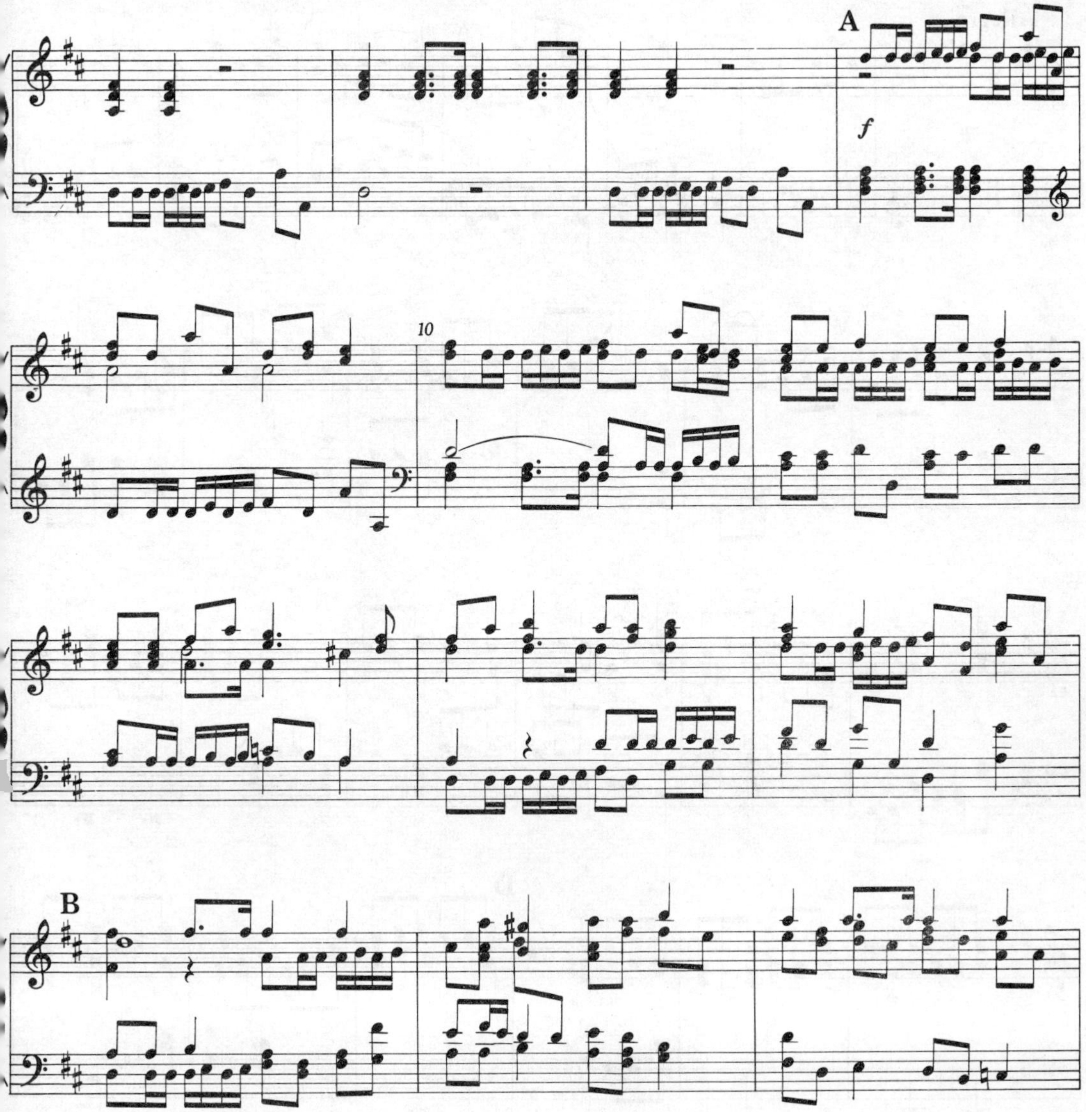
A
f
10
B
ff
20

ACT I
SCENE 2: SACRIFICE SCENE

SOLOS *(Bass, Tenor and Countertenor [or Tenor], and Soprano)* and CHORUS

sac-ri-fic'd, we have, we have, we have sac-ri-fic'd.

sac-ri-fic'd, we have, we have, we have sac-ri-fic'd.

sac-ri-fic'd, we have, we have, we have sac-ri-fic'd.

sac-ri-fic'd, we have, we have, we have sac-ri-fic'd.

TENOR **B** 20 *f*

Let our next ob-la-tion

dim. *mp* *soft*

be To Thor, thy thun - - - - - - d'ring son, Of such an-o-ther:

CHORUS

We have sac-ri-fic'd, we have sac-ri-fic'd, we have, we have, we have sac-ri-fic'd.

We have sac-ri-fic'd, we have sac-ri-fic'd, we have, we have, we have sac-ri-fic'd.

We have sac-ri-fic'd, we have sac-ri-fic'd, we have, we have, we have sac-ri-fic'd.

We have sac-ri-fic'd, we have sac-ri-fic'd, we have, we have, we have sac-ri-fic'd.

C

BASS

A third (of Fries-land breed was he) To Wo-den's wife, and to Thor's

mo-ther; and now, now, now we have, we have a - ton'd all three.

14

render,thanks,   thanks,   thanks,   thanks we ren-der,   to Wo-den our de-

Wo-den,   to Wo-den thanks we ren-der,   to Wo-den our de- fen-der,   to Wo-den our de-

Wo-den thanks we ren-der,   to   Wo-den thanks we ren-der,thanks we ren-der,   to   Wo-den our de-

render thanks we ren-der,   to Wo-den thanks we ren-der,   to Wo-den our de-

fen-der,   to Wo-den thanks we ren-der,thanks,   thanks, to Wo-den our de-fen-der,

fen-der,   to Wo-den thanks we ren-der,thanks, thanks,   to Wo-den our de-fen-der, thanks,

fen-der,thanks,   thanks,   thanks,   thanks,to Wo-den our de-fen-der,thanks,

fen-der,thanks,   thanks,   thanks, thanks,__ to Wo-den our de-fen-der,

E 70

thanks, thanks, thanks, thanks, to Wo-den our de-fen-der, to Wo-den our de- fen-der.

thanks, thanks, thanks, to Wo-den our de-fen-der, to Wo-den our de- fen-der.

thanks, thanks, thanks, to Wo-den our de-fen-der, to Wo-den our de- fen-der.

thanks, thanks, thanks, thanks, to Wo-den our de-fen-der, to Wo-den our de- fen-der.

p (Cont.)

7 Moderato

SOPRANO

mf 80

The lot is cast, and Tan-fan pleas'd; Of mor-tal cares you shall, you shall___ be

tr

eas'd, of mor-tal cares___ you shall _____ be eas'd.

8

22

170

laugh and dance, and quaff_ The juice that makes, the juice that makes the Bri - tons

soft   cresc.   tr

bold, The juice that makes, the juice that makes the Bri- tons bold.

p   cresc.   f

SOPRANO ff 180

To Wo -den's Hall, all, all to Wo -den's Hall, all, all, all, all to

ALTO   ff

To Wo -den's Hall, all, all to Wo-den's Hall, all, all, all, all to

TENOR   ff

To Wo -den 's Hall, all, all to Wo-den's Hall, all, all, all, all to

BASS   ff

To Wo -den's Hall, all, all to Wo-den's Hall, all, all, all, all to

ff (Strs)

Wo-den's Hall, all, all, Where in plen-teous, plen-teous bowls of bur-nish'd gold,

Wo -den's Hall all, all, Where in plen-teous, plen-teous bowls of bur-nish'd gold, We shall

Wo -den's Hall, all, all, Where in plen-teous, plen-teous bowls of bur-nish'd gold, We shall

Wo-den's Hall, all, all, Where in plen-teous, plen-teous bowls of bur-nish'd gold,

190

We shall laugh_ And dance and quaff, We shall laugh_ and dance and

laugh And dance and quaff, We shall laugh and dance, shall laugh and dance and

laugh, shall laugh And dance and quaff, We shall laugh and dance, We shall

We shall laugh And dance and quaff The juice that makes, that makes the Bri - tons

SOLO *(Tenor)* and CHORUS COME IF YOU DARE

10

SYMPHONY
Allegro

"Come, if you dare," our trum-pets sound, "Come, if you dare," the foes re - bound, "We

come, we come, we come, we come," Says the dou-ble,dou-ble,dou-ble beat of the thun - d'ring drum.

TENOR *f*   50

Now they charge on a - main, Now they ral - ly a-

beat of the thun - d'ring drum.

beat of the thun - d'ring drum.

beat of the thun - d'ring drum.

beat of the thun - d'ring drum.

d   *f* (Cont.)

gain. The gods from a - bove the mad — la - bour be - hold, And pi - ty man-

D

kind that will per - ish for gold, and pi - ty man - kind that will per - ish for

60   *soft*

p

The faint - ing Sax - ons quit their ground, Their trum - pets lan - guish

in their sound, They fly, they fly, they fly, they fly, "Vic - to - ria, Vic -

38

run, We re-turn to our lass - es like— for - tu - nate

trad - ers, Tri - umph-ant with spoils of the van-quish'd in-

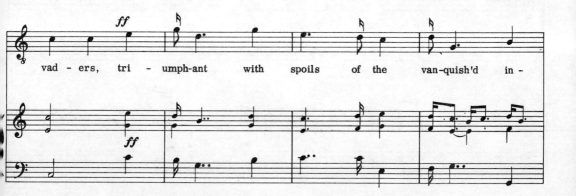

vad - ers, tri - umph-ant with spoils of the van-quish'd in-

40

FIRST ACT TUNE

ACT II
SCENE I

SOLO *(Soprano)* and DOUBLE CHORUS

HITHER, THIS WAY

12

✴ Originally ₵.

C

46

PHILADELL **D** *mf*

If you step no lon - ger

this way, this way bend.

this way, this way bend.

this way, this way bend.

this way, this way bend.

This way, hi - ther, this way, this way bend.

This way, hi - ther, this way, this way bend.

This way, hi - ther, this way, this way bend.

This way, hi - ther, this way, this way bend.

think - ing, Down _____ you

fall, a fur - long sin - king.

30

dim.

'Tis a fiend who has __ an-

cresc.

noy'd ye; Name but Heav'n, name but Heav'n and he'll a - void ye. Hi - ther

cresc.

48

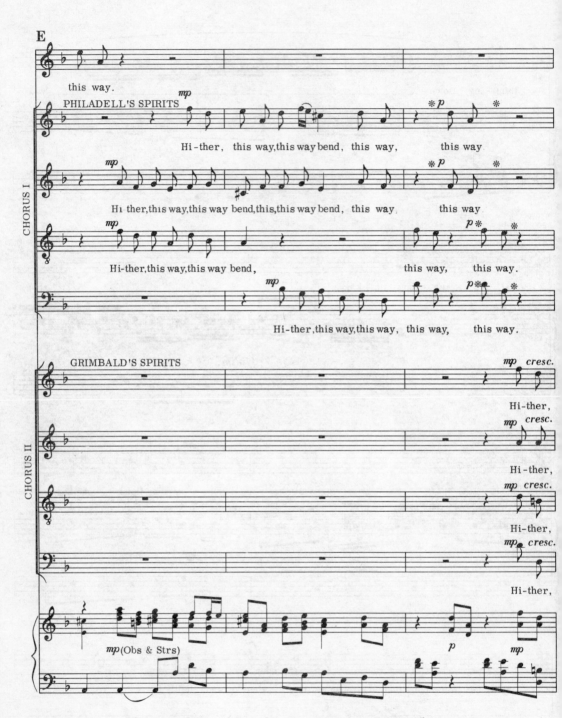

※ Notes between asterisks may be performed by Grimbald's (not Philadell's)Spirits (Ed.).

SOLO *(Bass)* LET NOT A MOONBORN ELF

13 Allegro
GRIMBALD

Let not a moon - born elf __ mis - lead ye, From your prey and

f (Cont.)

from __ your glo — ry: To fear, a – las, he has be – tray'd ye;

G *mf cresc.* 10

mf cresc.

Fol - low the flames that __ wave __ be-fore ye, Some-times sev'n and

f

H *mf cresc.*

mf cresc.

some-times one. Hur-ry, hur-ry, hur-ry, hur-ry, hur-ry, hur-ry, hur-ry,

20

f

mp cresc.

f

mp cresc.

Hur-ry, hur-ry, hur-ry on.

f (Vns)

See, see the

mf (Cont.)

foot - steps plain — ap - pear-ing. That — way Os - wald chose — for

fly - ing. Firm is the turf and fit for bear-ing, Where yon - der —

K*f*

dim.

f

dim.

pearl - y dews are ly - ing, Far he can - not

hence be gone. Hur-ry, hur-ry, hur-ry, hur-ry, hur-ry, hur-ry, hur-ry,

hurry, hurry, hurry on.

DOUBLE CHORUS HITHER, THIS WAY

* Notes between asterisks may be performed by Grimbald's spirits (Ed.).

M

fiend, trust not the ma-li-cious fiend. Hi - ther, this way, this way bend, this way,

fiend, trust not the ma-li-cious fiend. Hi-ther this way, this way bend, this, this way bend, this way,

fiend, trust not the ma-li-cious fiend. Hi-ther, this way, this way bend,

fiend, trust not the ma-li-cious fiend. Hi-ther this way, this way,

this way, hi-ther, this way, this way bend, this way, hi-ther, this way, this way bend.

this way, hi-ther, this way, this way bend, this way, hi-ther, this way, this way bend.

this way, this way, hi-ther, this way, this way bend, this way, hi-ther, this way, this way bend.

this way, this way, hi-ther, this way, this way bend, this way, hi-ther, this way, this way bend.

* Or   (Ed.).

SEPTET *(4 Sopranos, Countertenor [or Alto], Tenor and Bass)*
and CHORUS COME, FOLLOW ME

15

* In concert performances the Soprano III & IV parts may be performed by Philadell and Soprano II (Ed.).

* Or Philadell and Soprano II (Ed.).

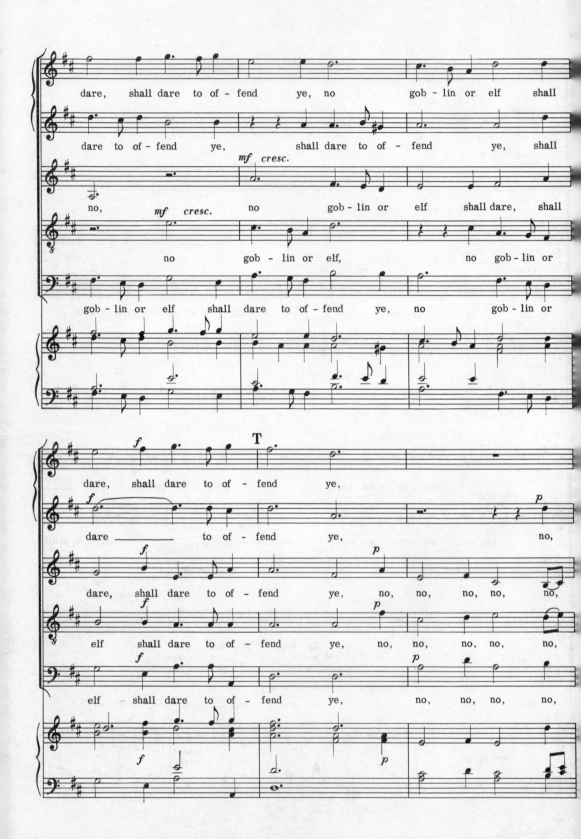

64

*SOPRANO II SOLO

We brethren of air   You he-roes will bear, We bre-thren of air   You

*SOPRANO III SOLO

We brethren of air   You he-roes will bear, We bre-thren of air   You

COUNTER TENOR [or TENOR or ALTO] SOLO

We brethren of air   You he-roes will bear, We bre-thren of air   You

he-roes will bear   To the kind and the fair,   the kind and the fair   that at - tend   ye.

he-roes will bear   To the kind and the fair,   the kind and the fair   that at - tend   ye.

he-roes will bear   To the kind and the fair,   the kind and the fair   that at - tend   ye.

* Or Philadell and Soprano II (Ed.).

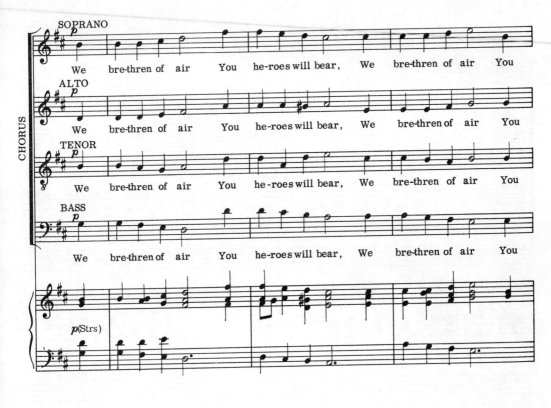

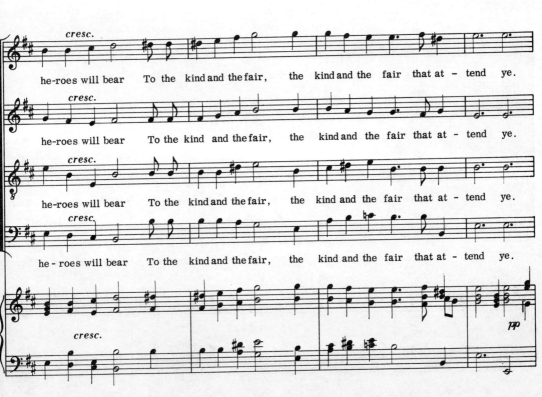

ACT II

SCENE 2

SOLO *(Tenor)* and CHORUS

HOW BLEST ARE SHEPHERDS

TENOR

1 How blest are shep-herds, how hap-py— their— lass-es,— While drums and
2 Bright nymphs of Bri-tain with gra-ces— at-tend-ed,— Let not your

(Cont.)
p (2nd verse mf)

30

1st time   2nd time

trum-pets are sound-ing— a-larms.   -larms.
days with-out plea-sure— ex-pire.   -pire.

cresc.

O — ver our low — ly sheds all the— storm— pass — es,—
Hon — our's but emp — ty, and when youth is— end — ed,—

p (2nd verse mp)

dim.   40

And when we die 'tis in each— o — ther's arms,
All men will praise you but none— will— de — sire.

mp (2nd verse mf)   dim.

70

72

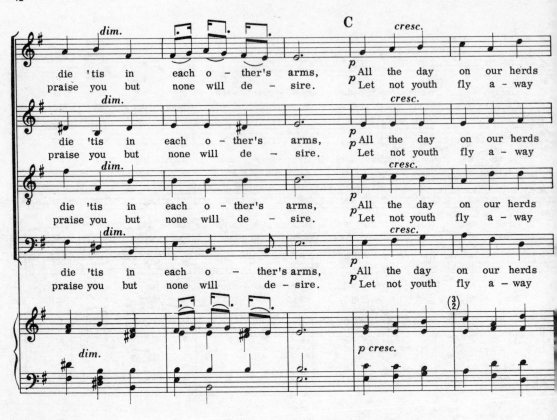

die 'tis in each o - ther's arms, p All the day on our herds
praise you but none will de - sire. p Let not youth fly a - way

70

and flocks em - ploy - ing, All the night mf f on our flutes and in en - joy - ing.
with - out con - tent - ing; Age will come f soon e - nough for your re - pent - ing.

DUET (2 Sopranos) SHEPHERD, SHEPHERD LEAVE DECOYING

17

SYMPHONY

Allegro

* ⊔ can be performed as ⊔˙ in first section (Ed.).

74

SOPRANO I

p

Shep-herd, shep-herd leave de-coy-ing: Pipes are sweet, on sum-mer's day,

SOPRANO II

p

Shep-herd, shep-herd leave de-coy-ing: Pipes are sweet, on sum-mer's day,

p (Cont.)

30   1st time   2nd time

But a lit-tle af-ter toy-ing, Wo-men have the shot to pay. shot to pay.

But a lit-tle af-ter toy-ing, Wo-men have the shot to pay. shot to pay.

cresc.

Here are mar-riage-vows for sign-ing: Set their marks that can-not write.

cresc.

Here are mar-riage-vows for sign-ing: Set their marks that can-not write.

cresc.

✻ ⌐ as before (Ed.).

E

After that, with — out re - pin - ing, Play, and— wel - come,

After that, with — out re - pin - ing, Play, and— wel - come,

40

day— and— night, Play, and— wel - come, play, and— wel — come,

day— and— night, _____ and night, play, and— wel - come,

┌ 1st time   ┌ 2nd time

play, _____ and wel - come, day and night. day and night.

play, _____ and wel-come, day— and night, day— and night.

CHORUS COME SHEPHERDS

* Alto and Tenor may use same words as Soprano here if preferred (Ed.).

mea-sure; The cares of wed - lock are cares of plea-sure.

mea-sure; The cares of wed - lock are cares of plea-sure.

mea - sure; The cares of wed - lock are cares of plea - sure.

mea - sure; The cares of wed - lock are cares of plea - sure.

But whe - ther mar-riage bring joy or sor - row, Make sure of

But whe - ther mar-riage bring joy or sor - row, Make sure of

But whe - ther mar-riage bring joy or sor - row, Make sure of

But whe - ther mar-riage bring joy or sor - row, Make sure of

78

this day, and hang to - mor-row, But whe-ther mar-riage bring joy_ or

this day, and hang to - mor-row, But whe-ther mar-riage bring joy or

this day, and hang to - mor-row, But whe-ther mar-riage bring joy or

this day, and hang to - mor-row, But whe-ther mar-riage bring joy or

sor-row, Make sure of this day, and hang to - mor - row.

sor-row, Make sure of this day, and hang to - mor - row.

sor -row, Make sure of this day, and hang to - mor - row.

sor -row, Make sure of this day, and hang to - mor - row.

HORNPIPE

SECOND ACT TUNE

AIR

19

81

ACT III
SCENE 2: FROST SCENE
CUPID (*Soprano*), COLD GENIUS (*Bass*) and CHORUS

20 PRELUDE [AS CUPID DECENDS]

Allegro moderato

what ho! liest thou a-sleep— be - neath those hills of snow? What ho! what ho! what

ho! Stretch———— out thy la - zy limbs; A-wake, a-wake, a - wake! And winter from thy

fur-ry man-tle shake; A-wake, a-wake,— And winter from thy fur-ry man-tle shake.

22

PRELUDE WHILE THE COLD GENIUS ARISES

Andante

p (Strs)

COLD GENIUS

What power art thou, who from below, Hast made me rise un-will-ing-ly and

slow, — From beds of ev-er-last — — ing snow?

See'st thou not how stiff, how stiff and won - drous

old, Far, far un-fit to bear the bit - ter cold, —

* For explanation of ⌇ see Preface.

D

I can scarce-ly move— or draw— my breath, can scarce-ly move— or draw— my

breath;— Let me, let me, let me freeze a - gain,— let me, let me freeze again to

death, let me, let me, let me, freeze— a-gain to death.

23. Presto

CUPID

Thou dot-ing fool, for - bear, for - bear! What dost thou mean by

freez-ing here? At Love's ap - pear - ing, All the sky clear - ing,

The storm-y winds their fu - ry spare. Thou dot-ing fool, for -

bear, for - bear! What dost thou mean by freez-ing here?

Win - ter sub - du - ing, And Spring re - new - ing, My beams cre -

ate a more glo - rious year. Thou dot - ing fool, for -

bear, for - bear! What dost thou mean by freez-ing here?

24 Allegro
COLD GENIUS

Great Love, I know thee now: Eld - est of the gods art

[8ves ad lib.]

thou! Heav'n and earth by thee were made, Heav'n and

88

27 CHORUS OF COLD PEOPLE

94

warm'd ye. In spite of cold weather I've brought ye to-geth er. 'Tis

I, 'tis I, 'tis I that have warm'd ye. 'Tis I, 'tis

I, 'tis I that have warm'd ye.

RITORNELLO %

warm'd us.

warm'd us.

warm'd us.

warm'd us.

260

T

p sim.

'Tis Love, 'tis Love, 'tis Love that has warm'd us. 'Tis Love, 'tis

p sim.

'Tis Love, 'tis Love, 'tis Love that has warm'd us. 'Tis Love, 'tis

p sim.

'Tis Love, 'tis Love, 'tis Love that has warm'd us. 'Tis Love, 'tis

p sim.

'Tis Love, 'tis Love, 'tis Love that has warm'd us. 'Tis Love, 'tis

sim.

p

270

cresc.

Love, 'tis Love that has warm'd us. In spite of cold wea-ther He

cresc.

Love, 'tis Love that has warm'd us. In spite of cold wea-ther He

cresc.

Love, 'tis Love that has warm'd us. In spite of cold wea-ther He

cresc.

Love, 'tis Love that has warm'd us. In spite of cold wea-ther He

cresc.

102

29 Animato (♩ = ♩)

CUPID

COLD GENIUS

Animato (♩ = ♩)

𝑓 (Vns)

A 𝑓

Sound a par - ley, ye fair, and sur - ren - der, sound, sound,

Sound, sound, sound, sound a par - ley, ye fair, and sur –

sound, sound, sound a par - ley, ye fair, sound _____ a par-ley, ye

ren - der,_ sound a par - ley, ye fair, sound a par _____ ley ye

* ⌒ can be performed as ♪♩. here and in corresponding bars (Ed.).

B

fair, and sur-ren-der. Set your-selves and your lo-vers at ease.

fair and sur-ren-der, Set your-selves and your lo-vers at ease.

Sound a par-ley, ye fair, and sur-ren-der,— sound, sound,

Sound, sound, sound, sound a par-ley, ye fair, and sur-

sound, sound, sound a par-ley, ye fair, sound ——————— a

ren-der,— sound a par-ley, ye fair, sound a par——————

370 par - ley, ye fair, sound _____ a par - ley, _ ye __

sound a par - ley, ye fair, sound a par _____ ley, ye

fair, and sur - ren - der. F mp Since the

fair, and sur - ren - der. Since the

380 fruit of de - sire is pos - sess - ing, 'Tis un - man - ly to sigh, 'tis un -

fruit of de - sire is pos - sess - ing. 'Tis un - man - ly to sigh, 'tis un -

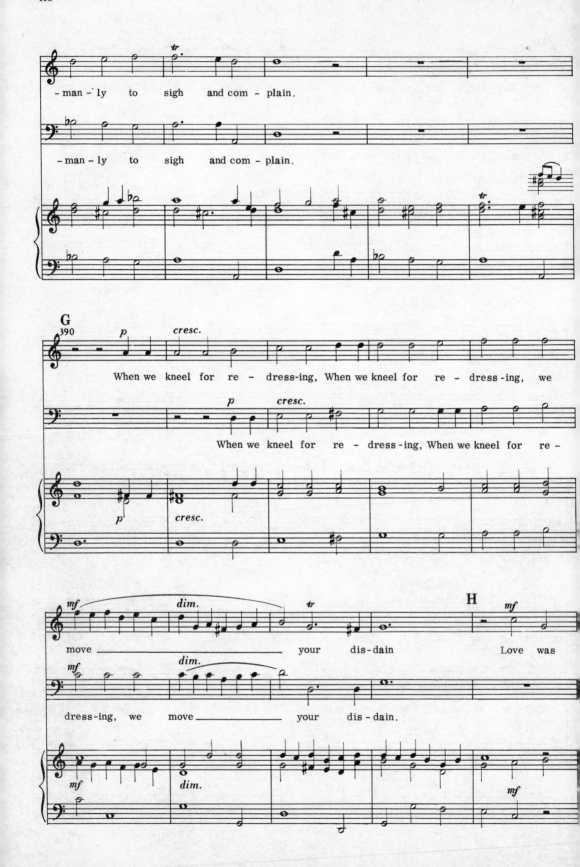

400

made, love was made for a bless - ing, — love was made, love was

Love was made, love was made, love was made for a bless - ing, —

made for a bless_____ ing And

cresc.

love was made for a bless-ing, was made for a__ bless - ing And

cresc.

410

f K **p** *cresc.*

not for__ a pain. Love was made for a bless_____

f **p** *cresc.*

not for a pain. Love was made for a bless-ing, was

f **p** *cresc.*

ing And not for a pain.

made for a bless - ing And not for a pain.

THIRD ACT TUNE

HORNPIPE

ACT IV

DUET *(2 Sopranos)* TWO DAUGHTERS

114

PASSACAGLIA

SOLO (*Countertenor* [*or Tenor*]) and CHORUS **HOW HAPPY THE LOVER**
DUET (*Soprano and Bass*), TRIOS and CHORUS **FOR LOVE**

COUNTERTENOR [or TENOR]

How hap—py the lo—ver, How ea—sy his chain, how

hap - py the lo - ver, how ea - sy his chain! How sweet, how

sweet to dis - co - ver He_ sighs not in vain. How sweet to dis-

co - ver He_ sighs not in vain.

SOPRANO

How hap - py the lov - er, How ea - sy his

ALTO

How hap - py the lov - er, How ea - sy his

TENOR

How hap - py the lov - er, How ea - sy_ his_

BASS

How hap - py the lov - er, How ea - sy his

* Chorus may start here.

118

sweet to dis - cov - er— He— sighs not in vain.

sweet to dis - cov - er He sighs not in vain.

sweet to dis - cov - er He sighs not in vain.

sweet to dis - cov - er He sighs not in vain.

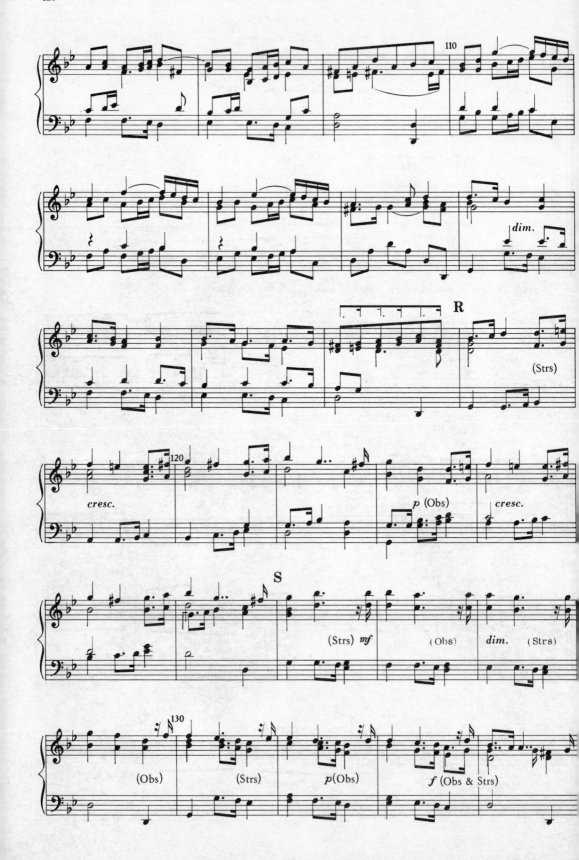

3 WOMEN

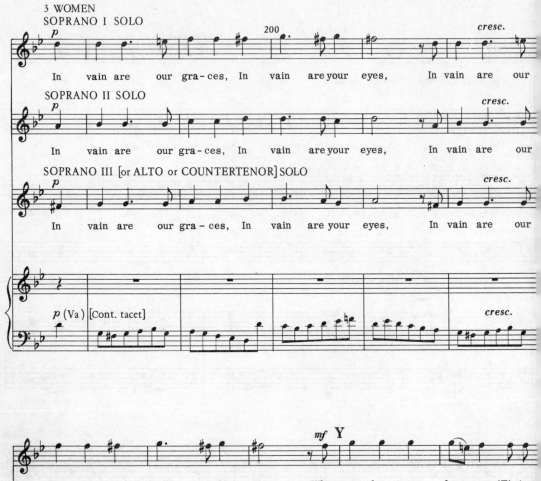

late   to be   wise,   'tis too late,   too late,   'tis,'tis too late   to be   wise.

late   to be   wise,   'tis too late,   too late,   'tis,'tis too late   to be   wise.

late   to be   wise,   'tis too late,   too late,   'tis,'tis too late   to be   wise.

3   INVOLVGA

3 MEN

COUNTERTENOR [or TENOR] SOLO

Then   use   the sweet   bless-ing, then   use   the sweet   bless-ing While   now   in pos -

TENOR SOLO

Then   use   the sweet   bless-ing, then   use   the sweet   bless-ing While   now   in pos -

BASS SOLO

Then   use   the sweet   bless-ing, then   use   the sweet   bless-ing While   now   in pos -

mp(Cont.)

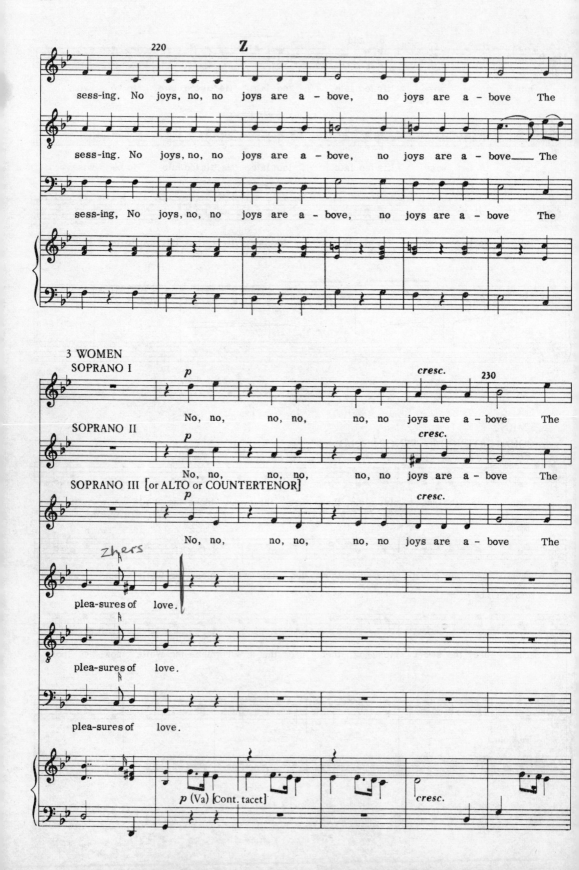

plea-sures, the plea-sures, the plea - sures of love.

plea-sures, the plea-sures, the plea - sures of love.

plea-sures, the plea-sures, the plea-sures of love.

No, no, no, no, no, no

No, no, no, no, no

No, no, no, no, no, no

No, no, no, no, no

mf (Obs & Strs)

joys are a - bove The plea-sures, the plea-sures, the plea-sures of love.

FOURTH ACT TUNE
AIR

33

Allegro leggiero

ACT V
[CONSORT OF TRUMPETS]
TRUMPET TUNE

SOLO *(Bass)* YE BLUST'RING BRETHREN

C

tire, and let Bri – tan – nia rise,___ re-tire, re-tire, and let Bri-tan – nia

p sempre dim.

rise, In tri – – – – – – – umph o'er the main.

pp

Andante

Se-rene and calm_____ and void___ of fear,

p (Recs)

se-rene_ and calm_____ and void___ of

fear, The Queen of Islands, the Queen of Is-lands must ap – pear, Se-rene and

calm, _____ se-rene and calm, _____ and void of fear, the Queen of

Is-lands must ap – pear, se-rene and calm, _____

se-rene and calm, _____ and void of fear the Queen of Is-lands must ap – pear.

SYMPHONY

DUET *(Soprano and Bass)* and CHORUS ROUND THY COAST

Round thy__ coast, fair nymph of Bri‑tain, For thy guard our wa‑ters__ flow:

PAN

Round thy coast, fair nymph of Brit‑tain, For thy guard our wa‑ters flow:____

cresc.

Pro - teus, all — his herd ad-mit-ting On_ thy green to_ graze be-low:

cresc.

Pro - teus all his herd ad-mit-ting_ On_ thy green to graze be-low:

cresc.

mf

For - eign lands thy fish_ are_ tast - ing; Learn from thee lux - u - rious fast - ing;

mf

For - eign lands thy fish are tast - ing;_ Learn from thee lux - u - rious fast - ing;

mf

p

30

For - eign lands thy fish are_ tast - ing; Learn from thee lux - u - rious fast - ing.

p

For - eign lands thy fish are tast - ing, Learn from thee lux - u - rious fast - ing.

p

138

TRIO *(Countertenor [or Tenor], Tenor and Bass)* FOR FOLDED FLOCKS

38

no, no, no, no, no, no, no, no, no mines can more of wealth sup-ply, It keeps, it

no, no, no, no, no, no, no, no, no, no mines can more of wealth sup-ply, It keeps, it

no, no, no, no, no, no, no mines can more, can more of wealth sup-ply, It keeps, it

keeps the peasants from the cold, And takes, and takes for kings the Ty-rian dye.

keeps the peasants from the cold, And takes, and takes for kings the Ty-rian dye.

keeps the peasants from the cold, And takes, and takes for kings the Ty-rian dye.

144

SOLO *(Tenor[or Bass])* and TRIO *(Tenor [or Bass] and 2 Basses)*

YOUR HAY IT IS MOW'D

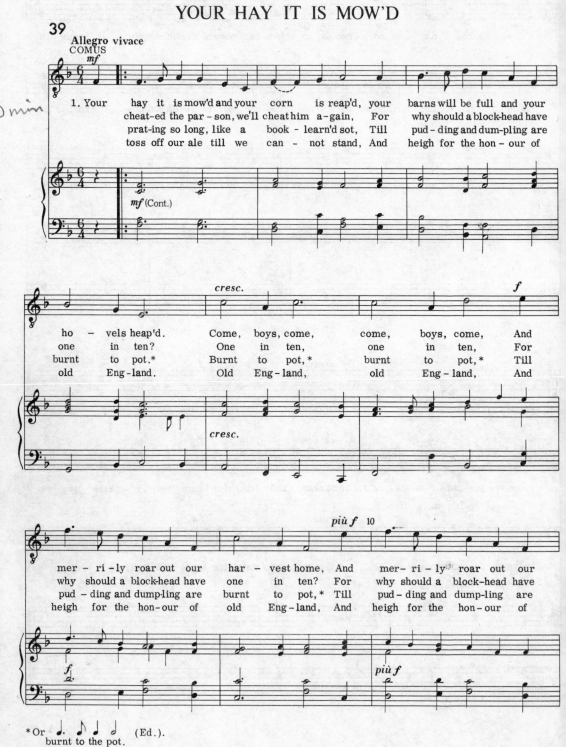

39

Allegro vivace

COMUS

mf

D min

1. Your hay it is mow'd and your corn is reap'd, your barns will be full and your
cheat-ed the par-son, we'll cheat him a-gain, For why should a block-head have
prat-ing so long, like a book-learn'd sot, Till pud-ding and dum-pling are
toss off our ale till we can-not stand, And heigh for the hon-our of

mf (Cont.)

cresc.   *f*

ho — vels heap'd. Come, boys, come, come, boys, come, And
one in ten? One in ten, one in ten, For
burnt to pot.* Burnt to pot,* burnt to pot,* Till
old Eng-land. Old Eng-land, old Eng-land, And

cresc.

più f 10

mer-ri-ly roar out our har-vest home, And mer-ri-ly roar out our
why should a block-head have one in ten? For why should a block-head have
pud-ding and dump-ling are burnt to pot,* Till pud-ding and dump-ling are
heigh for the hon-our of old Eng-land, And heigh for the hon-our of

f   *più f*

*Or ♩ ♪ ♪ ♩ (Ed.).
   burnt to the pot.

145

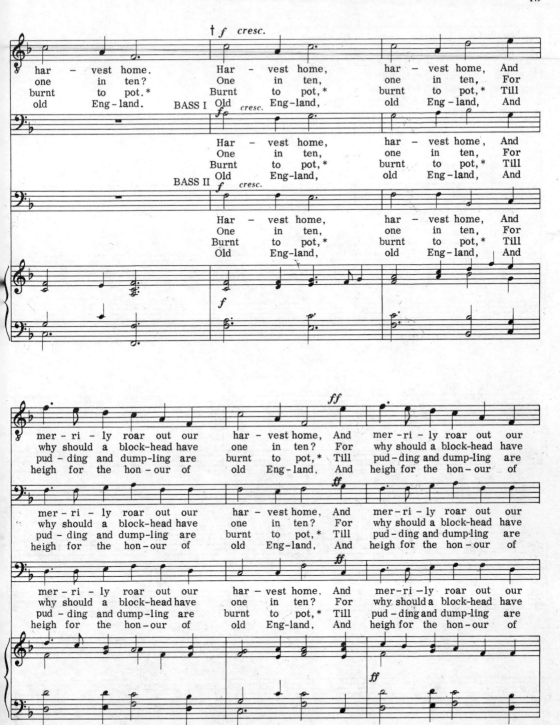

† This Trio may be performed by the Chorus if desired (Ed.).

*Or 𝅘𝅥𝅭 𝅘𝅥𝅮 𝅘𝅥𝅮 𝅗𝅥 (Ed.).
   burnt to the pot.

146

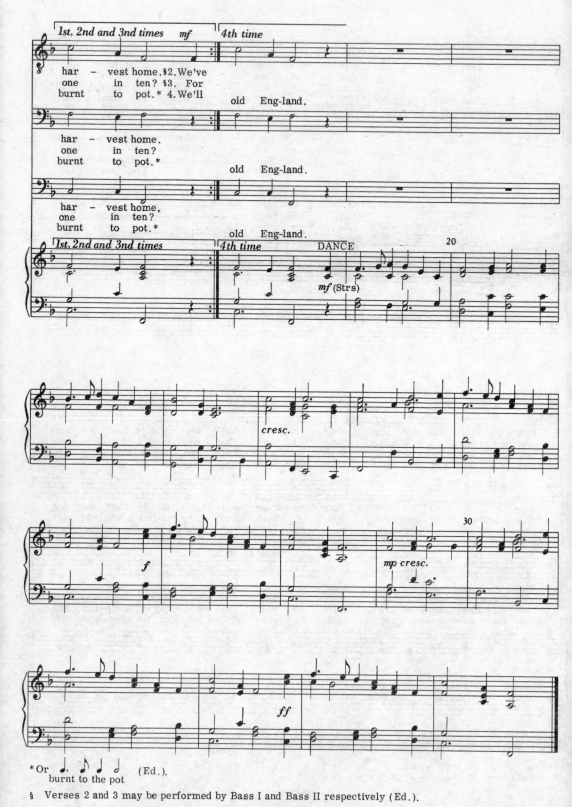

*Or 𝅘𝅥. 𝅘𝅥𝅮 𝅘𝅥 𝅘𝅥 (Ed.).
  burnt to the pot

§ Verses 2 and 3 may be performed by Bass I and Bass II respectively (Ed.).

SOLO *(Soprano)* FAIREST ISLE

VENUS

Fair-est isle, all isles___ ex – cel – ling, Seat___ of plea – sure

and— of love. Ve - nus here will choose— her dwell – ing,

And— for - sake— her Cy – prian grove. Cu - pid from his

fa - v'rite na - tion, Care— and en - vy will— re - move.

Jea - lous - y that poi – sons pas – sion, And— de - spair— that

dies___ for love. Gen - tle mur - murs, sweet___ com - plain - ing,

Sighs___ that blow___ the fire___ of love. Soft re - pul - ses,

kind___ dis - dain - ing, Shall___ be all___ the pains___ you prove;

Ev - 'ry swain shall pay his du - ty, Grate - ful ev - 'ry

nymph___ shall prove; And as these ex - cel___ in___

beau - ty, Those___ shall be___ re - nown'd___ for love.

DIALOGUE *(Soprano and Bass)* YOU SAY 'TIS LOVE

SHE

You say 'tis love___ creates the pain, Of which so sad ___ ___

- ly you complain, And yet would fain engage my heart In that un-

ea - sy cru – el, cru – – el part; But how, a-las! _____

_____ how, a-las! think you that I Can bear the wounds _____ of ___ which you

die? How, a-las! _____ how, a-las! think you that I Can bear the wounds of which you die?

Animato (♩.=♩)

HE *mf*

'Tis not my pas - sion makes my care, But your in - dif - f'rence

gives___ de - spair; The lust — y Sun, the lust — y Sun be -

gets no Spring, Till gen — tle show'rs, till gen — tle show'rs as -

sist — ance bring; So Love, that scorch - es and___ de - stroys, Till

kind - ness aids, till kind - ness aids, can cause___ no joys.

SHE

Love has a thou-sand, thou - sand, thou-sand, thou - sand ways to please,

Love has a thou-sand, thou - sand, thou-sand, thou - sand ways to please, But more, more, more,

more, more, more, more, more to rob us of our ease, But more, more, more, more, more, more, more to

rob us of our ease. For wak - ing nights, and care - ful

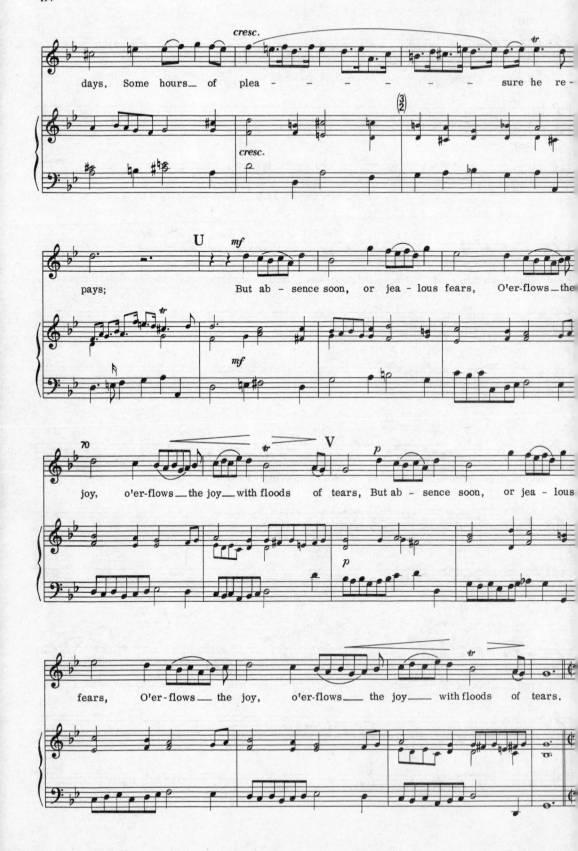

Moderato (♩=♩.)
HE *p*

But one soft moment makes a-mends   For all the tor —ment that attends,

mp

dim.   *poco rit.*

One soft moment makes a - mends For all the tor — — ment that   at -
poco rit.

mp

dim.

Allegretto (♩.=♩)
SHE *f*

Let us love, ____ let us love and to hap-pi-ness haste, ___ haste, ___

tends. ____ Let us love, ____ let us love, and to hap-pi-ness haste, ___ haste, ___
Allegretto (♩.=♩)

f

90 *p*

haste, ___ haste, ___ haste, ____ let us love, ____ let us love, and to hap - pi - ness

haste, ___ haste, ___ haste, ____ let us love, ____ let us love, and to hap - pi - ness

p

*Or 𝅗𝅥 𝅘𝅥 (Ed.).

Z

120

faith - ful love,— than faith - ful love,— and kind, and kind pos - sess - ing, and

- sess - ing, than faith - ful love,— and kind, and kind pos - sess - ing, and

cresc. *dim.*

kind,———————————————— and kind, and kind pos - sess - ing.

cresc. *dim.*

kind,———————————————— and kind, and kind pos - sess - ing.

[WARLIKE CONSORT]
TRUMPET TUNE

42 Vivace

f (Tpts & Strs)

10

mf

cresc.

ff

[attacca]

SOLO *(Soprano)* and CHORUS SAINT GEORGE

Pa — tron of _____ our Isle! Saint George, a sol — dier and _____ a

Saint! On this, this au - spicious or - der smile,

On this, this au - spicious or - der smile! Which

love _____ and arms will plant, Saint

will plant, On this, this au - spicious or - der smile!

Which love and arms ⸺ will plant.

* Or D (Ed.).

*Or D (Ed.).

Choral Music
OF THE 16th & 17th CENTURIES

Giovanni Gabrieli

IN ECCLESIIS
motet for soloists, chorus, strings, instruments & organ.
Edited by Denis Stevens

Claudio Monteverdi

BEATUS VIR
for SSATTB chorus, instruments & organ. Edited by John Steele

MAGNIFICAT
for soloists, double choir, organ & orchestra.
Edited by John Steele & Denis Stevens

VESPERS
for soloists, double choir, organ & orchestra.
Edited by Denis Stevens

Giovanni da Palestrina

MISSA PAPAE MARCELLI
for unaccompanied SSATBB chorus. Edited by Otto Goldschmidt

STABAT MATER
motet for unaccompanied double choir. Edited by W. Barclay Squire

---

Giovanni Rovetta

LAUDATE DOMINUM
for SS(A)A(T)TB chorus, instruments & organ. Edited by John Steele

---

Alessandro Scarlatti

AUDI FILIA
for SSA solo, SSATB chorus, instruments, string orchestra & organ.
Edited by John Steele

ST CECILIA MASS (1720)
for SSATB soli & chorus, string orchestra & organ.
Edited by John Steele

Heinrich Schütz

THE PASSION
a selection from the 'Four Passions'. ATB soli, chorus & organ

novello WD